•PARRAGON•

3-D MASKS

DINOSAURS

Model engineering by Pat Doyle
Colour artworks by Blackjacks
Other illustrations by Graham Osborne
Text by Karen Farrington

Dinosaurs

Millions of years ago giant beasts roamed the earth. Hard to imagine, isn't it, reptiles the size of buses living in swamps where cities now stand? Even the shape of the world's continents was different. It was long before human beings existed. There are still many unanswered questions about dinosaurs and we can only try to imagine what life was like then.

In the Beginning...

Earth came into existence some 4,600 million years ago. In the beginning it was nothing more than a spinning ball of gas and dust. Gradually the particles joined together to make a solid planet. The first 4,000 million years of the Earth's life are called the Pre-Cambrian period.

It took 1,000 million years for the first oceans to form. At this time, you would not have recognised the earth's surface. Rivers of molten lava poured from the numberless spouting volcanoes. The usually dark skies could be dramatically lit up by violent flashes of lightning. Showers of comets or meteorites crashed on to the surface. The air itself was poisonous and unbreathable. Yet amid all this chaos the first simple living things began to appear – organisms which could reproduce themselves.

The First Life

The next period, from 600 to 245 million years ago, is called the Palaeozoic (ancient

life) period. In it, tiny water-borne animals, such as conches, shellfish and the very earliest fish, multiplied in the seas and began to live on land. At this stage, the first animals with backbones, called vertebrates, began to emerge.

About 245 million years ago the Mesozoic (middle life) period started which itself is divided into three further periods: Triassic, Jurassic and Cretaceous. At this point the first dinosaurs appeared and they dominate the Mesozoic Age.

During the Triassic period which lasted some 45 million years, the earth was one huge continent and there were no polar ice caps or seasons. The weather was constantly temperate, which suited the early dinosaurs. They were small and could move on two legs or four.

In the Jurassic period the huge continent split into two – changing the weather. It rained more and became cooler. Early flying dinosaur species evolved. The birds which fly around today are almost certainly the closest living relatives to dinosaurs.

The Cretaceous period began 145 million years ago and lasted for 80 million years. Dinosaurs were still making their way around the world across land bridges which were vanishing rapidly as the earth continued to break up into the continents we know today. This period ended with the extinction of the dinosaurs about 65 million years ago.

Finding Fossils

What is a Dinosaur?

The word 'dinosaur' means 'terrible lizard'. Not every huge prehistoric creature is called a dinosaur. A true dinosaur lived on land, but winged reptiles, such as the pterosaur, were very similar. A typical dinosaur had straight legs which tucked beneath its body. Some had hips like a lizard while others had hips like a bird. They probably laid eggs in the same way as reptiles today. Some of the dinosaurs that lived all those years ago were as big as 20 elephants! Others were smaller – but as even these were about the size of a donkey, it is clear that for some reason they were huge compared to all life on earth today.

Fossils and Footprints

Nobody guessed that dinosaurs had even existed until 1820, when huge bones and teeth were found in a quarry in southern England. These items were so enormous that the man who found them, Gideon Mantell, knew they must have belonged to a group of creatures as yet unknown. As he thought the bones were like those of an iguana lizard, he called this new discovery Iguanodon.

The word 'dinosaur' was invented in 1841 by Dr Richard Owen, who became the first director of the Natural History Museum in London. Since then scientists and historians have pieced together many other bones discovered in Europe, North America,

Africa and Asia to create the skeletons of dinosaurs. This gives us an idea of the size and shape of many, but it is almost impossible to know what colour they were.

The biggest clues left behind are fossils. A fossil occurs when an animal like a dinosaur dies. Its body is be covered by the sediment of a river and its flesh rots away. Soon the sediment hardens into a surface of rock. Much later the fossil may be revealed, after wind, rain and sea have erased the top layer of rock. People who study fossils are called palaeontologists.

Discovering the Bones

A palaeontologist has to dig to find fossils, which are fragile things, often embedded in earth and rocks. These must be removed carefully before the fossil is dug up, which may mean using anything from a brush to a pneumatic drill. Before a find is removed from a site, its exact position is noted down. A fossil's position and depth in the layers of rock can tell a fossil-hunter when the creature lived.

In the laboratory scientists can work out what the dinosaur looked like. It is a specialists' job to re-assemble the skeleton, usually without a full set of bones.

Besides dinosaur bones, footprints can be found, surviving from millions of years ago. These imprints have been covered by sand or water and preserved for ever. There may also be signs of dragging left by the tail.

Scraps of dinosaur skin have been recovered, which suggest that dinosaurs were grey, brown, or greenish in colour.

Eating and Drinking

Most of the big dinosaurs depended for their food on the lush vegetation which abounded in the Mesozoic period. The largest of the dinosaurs, such as the Apatosaurus in the Jurassic period, would eat a ton of plants a day. Many had long necks which enabled them to graze on the tenderest leaves high in the trees.

Some dinosaurs had a gizzard, a thick-walled muscular pocket in the gut, with a tough lining to grind up food. This sort of dinosaur would have regularly swallowed gravel and stones (also known as 'gastroliths', or 'gizzard stones'). The food which passed into the gizzard would be ground down by the pebbles which were moved about by muscles. That way the food was reduced to a mash before it reached the intestines. When the stones were worn down, the dinosaur would vomit them out and find new ones.

Other plant-eaters relied on their pointed teeth to chew the food to a pulp. Fossilised jaws reveal that they would grind up food much as plant-eating animals do today. However, they had considerably more teeth. An Edmontosaurus, for example, had

as many as 1,000 teeth with which to crush its food.

Horned dinosaurs which also lived on plants had a beak-like arrangement for a mouth. They would chop food finely with their scissor-like teeth. Plant-eaters often had broad hands with short fingers and claws with which to tug at the greenery.

Meat-eaters, such as the Tyrannosaurus, had either to kill another animal for their food or scavenge from carcasses. Like today's predators (tigers or wolves, for example), these dinosaurs would trail groups of peaceful plant-eaters, looking for weaklings. An old member of the herd, or perhaps a very young one, would sooner or later make the fatal mistake of leaving the safety of the herd. The meat-eater was then ready to pounce, tearing at the flesh of its victim with razor-like teeth. It would swallow the flesh whole without chewing, to consume as much of the meat as possible in the shortest possible time. It never knew when its next meal would be.

Not all the meat-eaters were big. Some of the most vicious were much smaller. Their prey included insects, lizards and the small mammals then around. They had long, sharp claws, dagger-like teeth and could move much faster than bigger dinosaurs.

Some dinosaurs were omnivorous, that is, they ate both plants and meat, as bears do today.

The Great Dinosaurs

Dilophosaurus

(dylo-foh-sawros)

The Dilophosaurus was one of the earliest large carnivorous dinosaurs, appearing about 200 million years ago and dying out about 40 million years later. It boasted a very unusual crest on its head made from two thin ridges of bone situated side by side. These were shaped like semi-circles and have long baffled palaeontologists, for they were far too weak to be used as weapons. Possibly they were used to signal to other dilophosaurs.

Unlike the far more formidable Tyrannosaurus which came later, the Dilophosaurus seems to have had weak and slender jaws. This means it would probably not have had the strength to deal with struggling live prey. It was probably therefore simply a scavenger, living off already dead prey, rather than a hunter of live creatures.

Triceratops

(try-ser-a-tops)

One of the most distinctive of all the dinosaurs, Triceratops boasted three large horns – a small one on its snout and two larger ones above its eyebrows – and a large bony frill at the back of its head. Both the horns and the frill were to defend it against marauding carnivores.

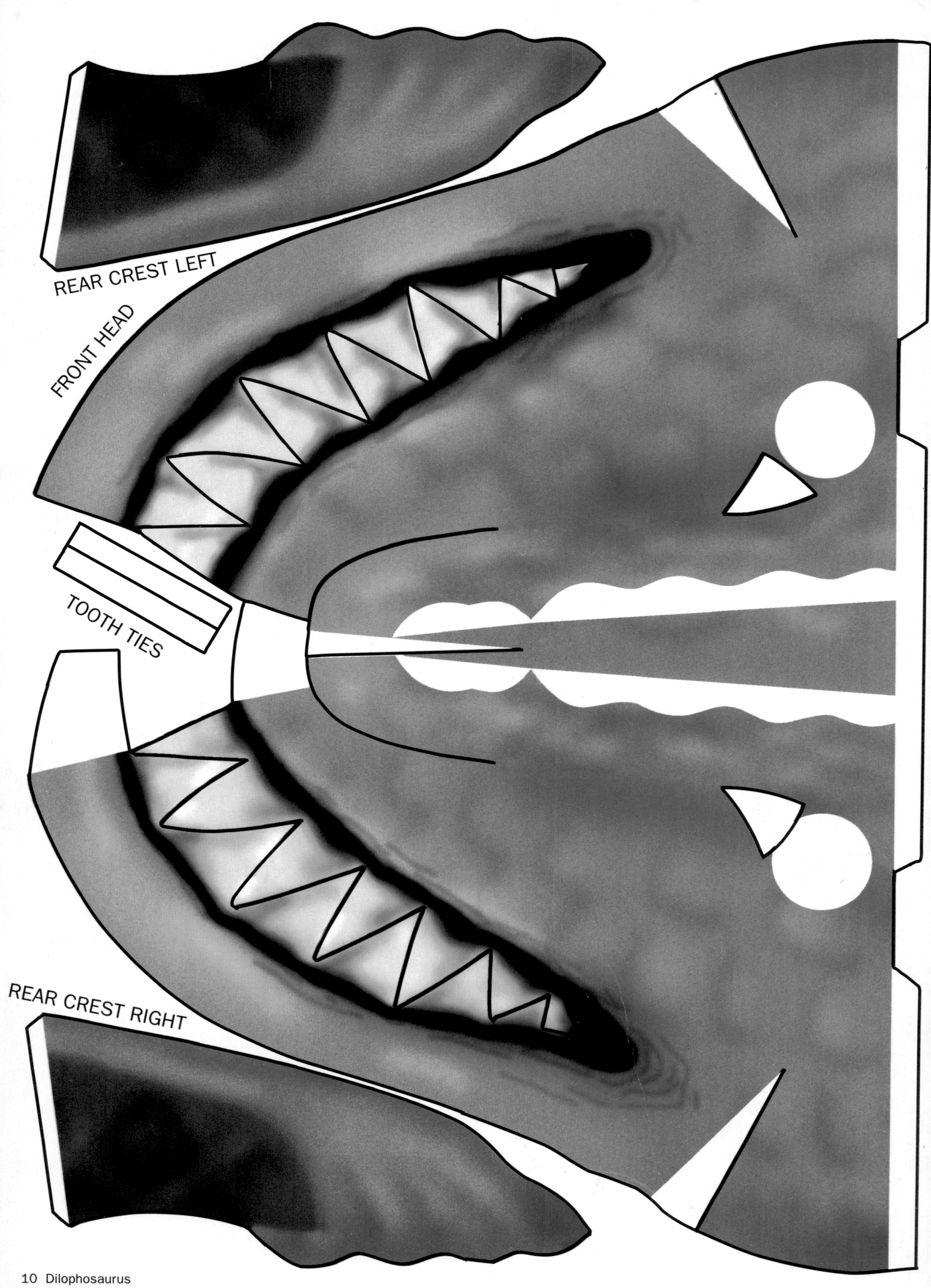
REAR CREST LEFT
FRONT HEAD
TOOTH TIES
REAR CREST RIGHT

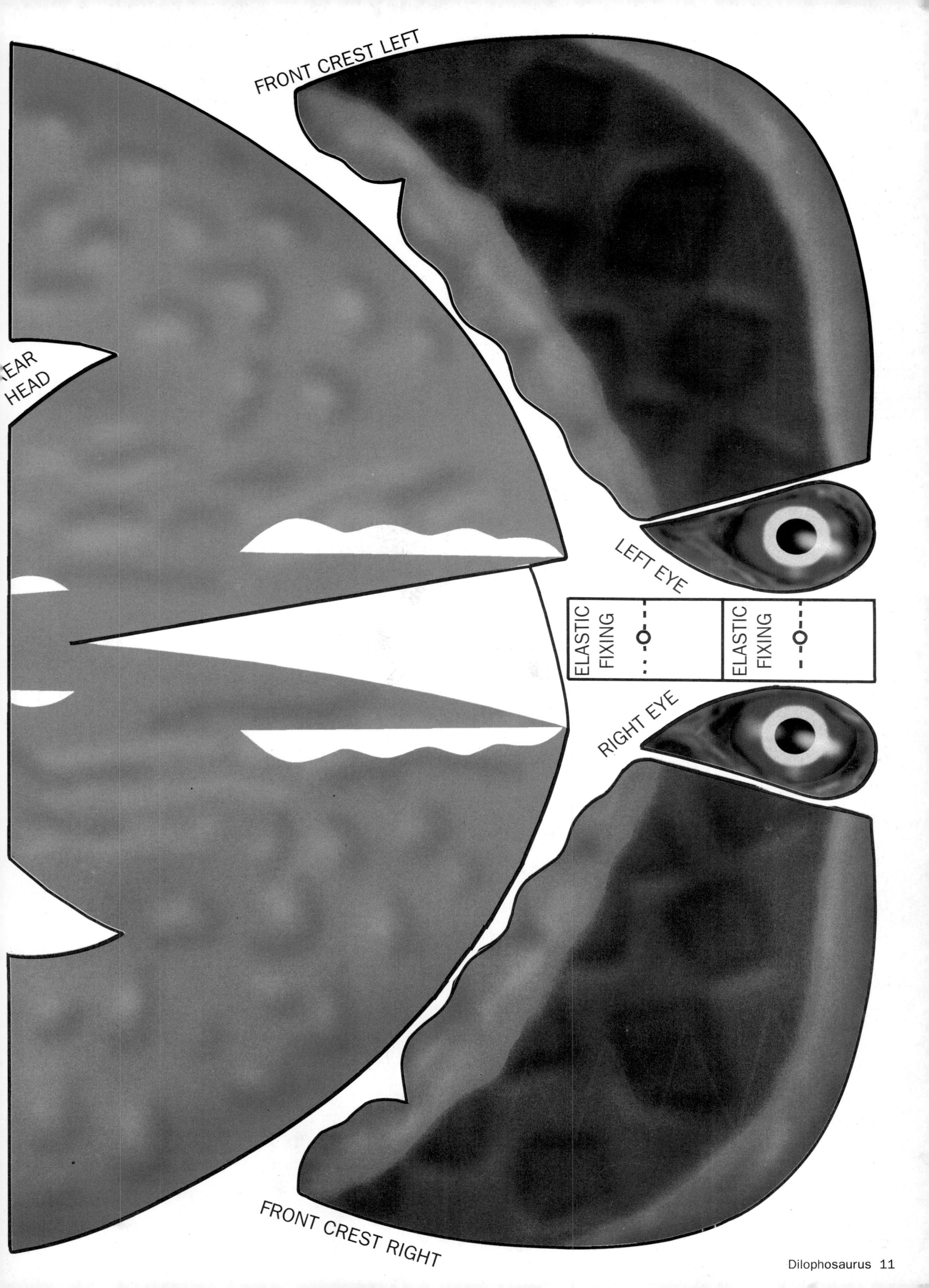
FRONT CREST LEFT
REAR
HEAD
LEFT EYE
ELASTIC FIXING
ELASTIC FIXING
RIGHT EYE
FRONT CREST RIGHT

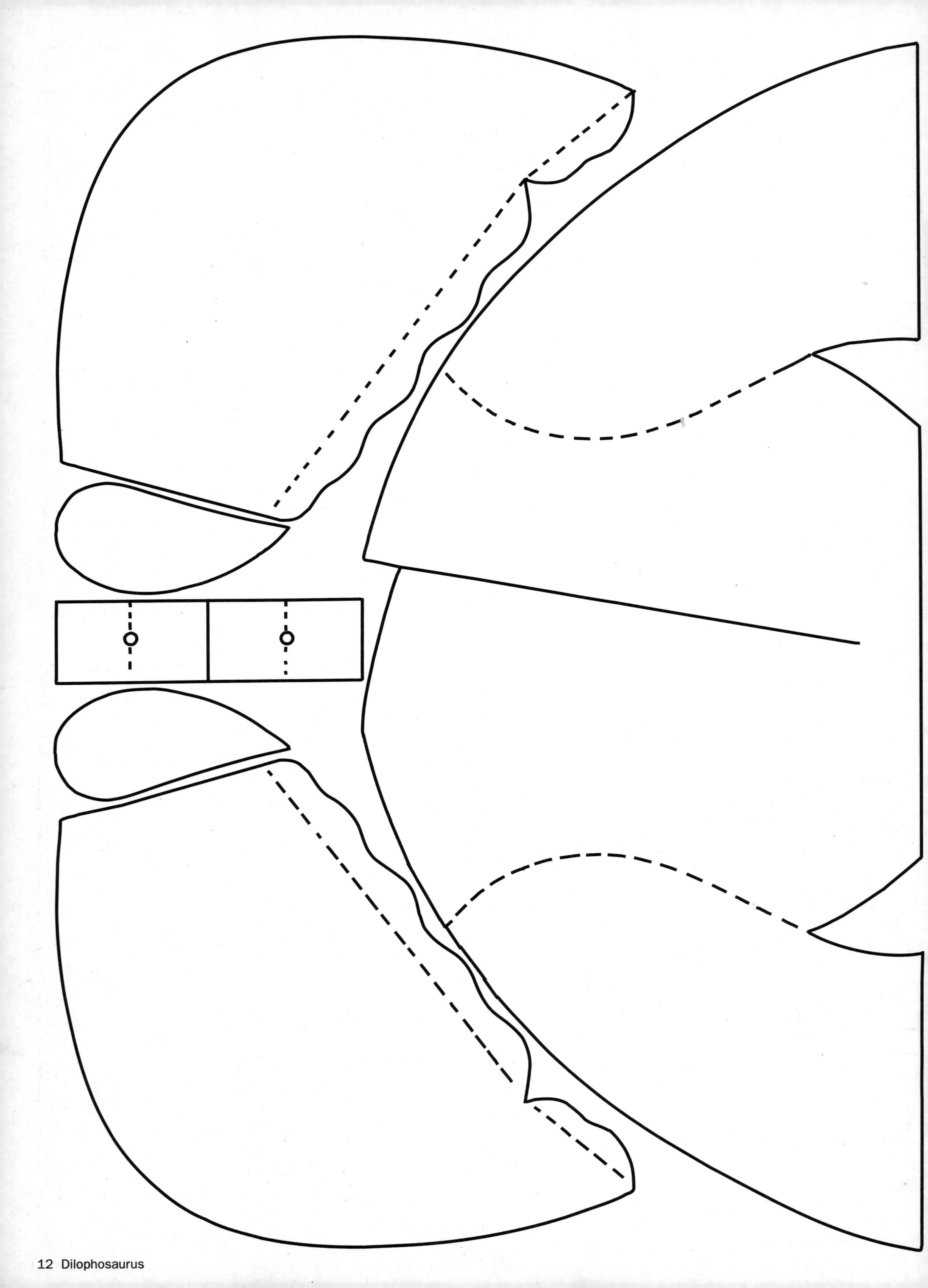

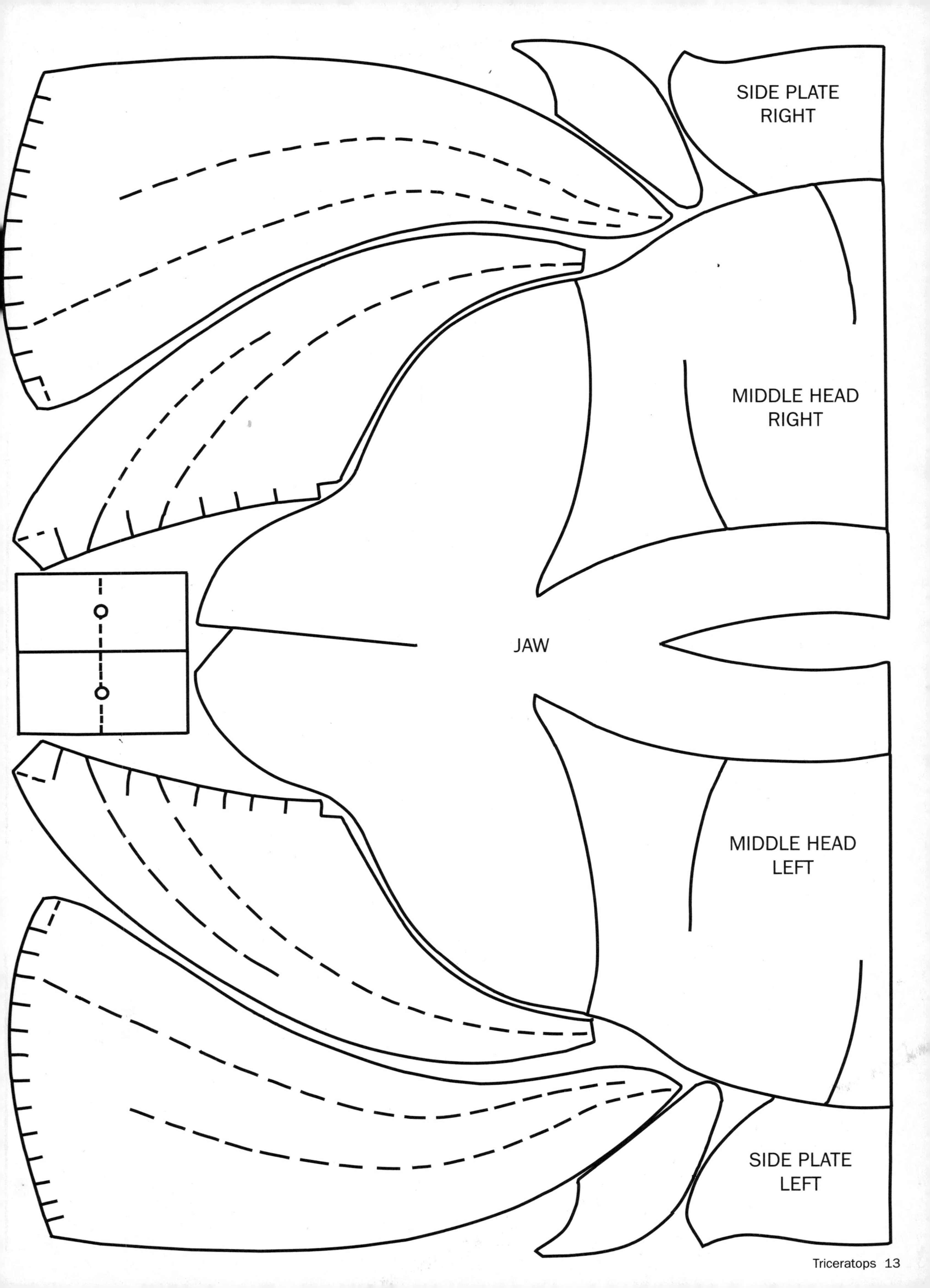
SIDE PLATE
RIGHT
MIDDLE HEAD
RIGHT
JAW
MIDDLE HEAD
LEFT
SIDE PLATE
LEFT

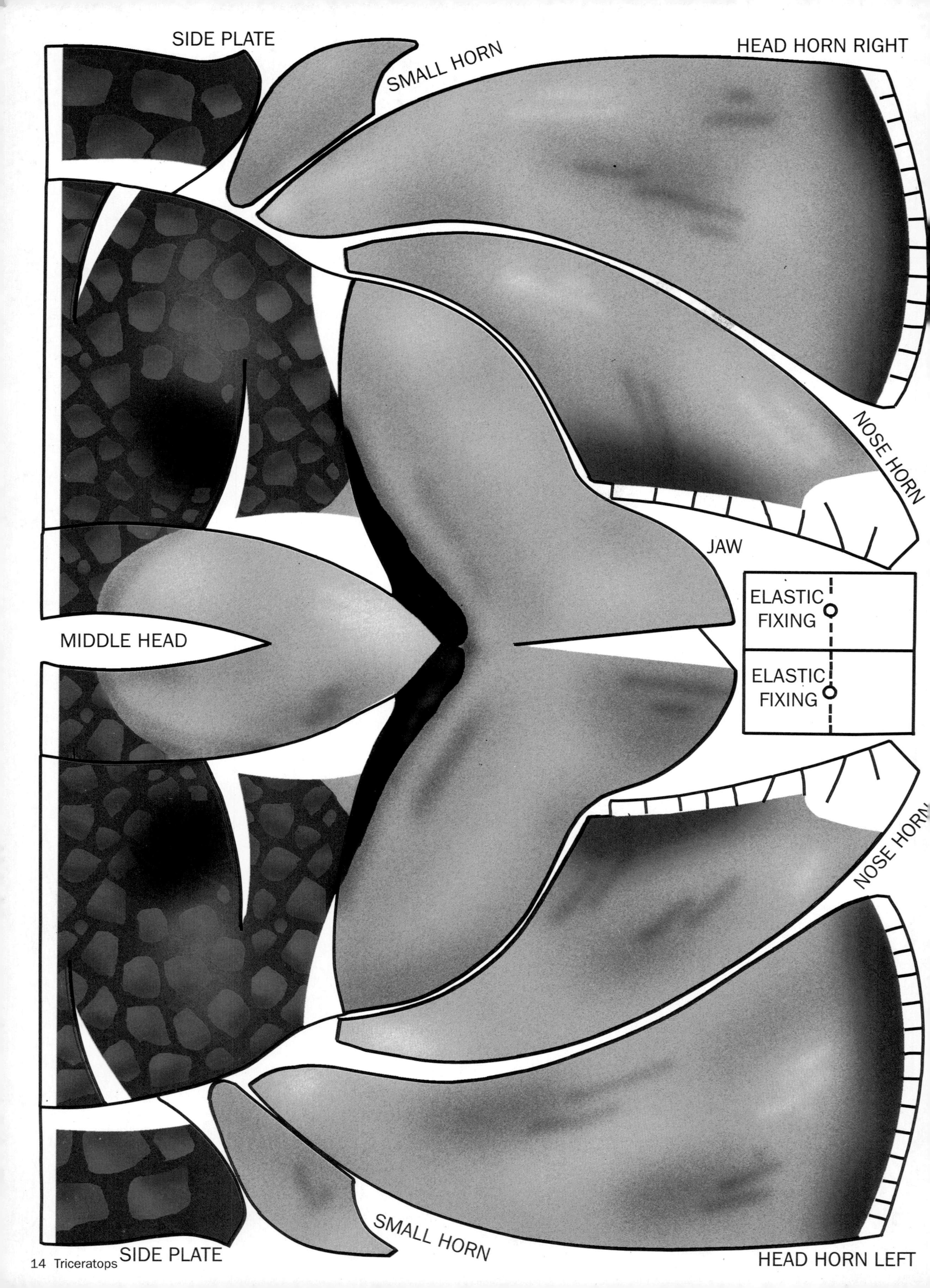
SIDE PLATE
SMALL HORN
HEAD HORN RIGHT
NOSE HORN
JAW
ELASTIC FIXING
ELASTIC FIXING
MIDDLE HEAD
NOSE HORN
SIDE PLATE
SMALL HORN
HEAD HORN LEFT

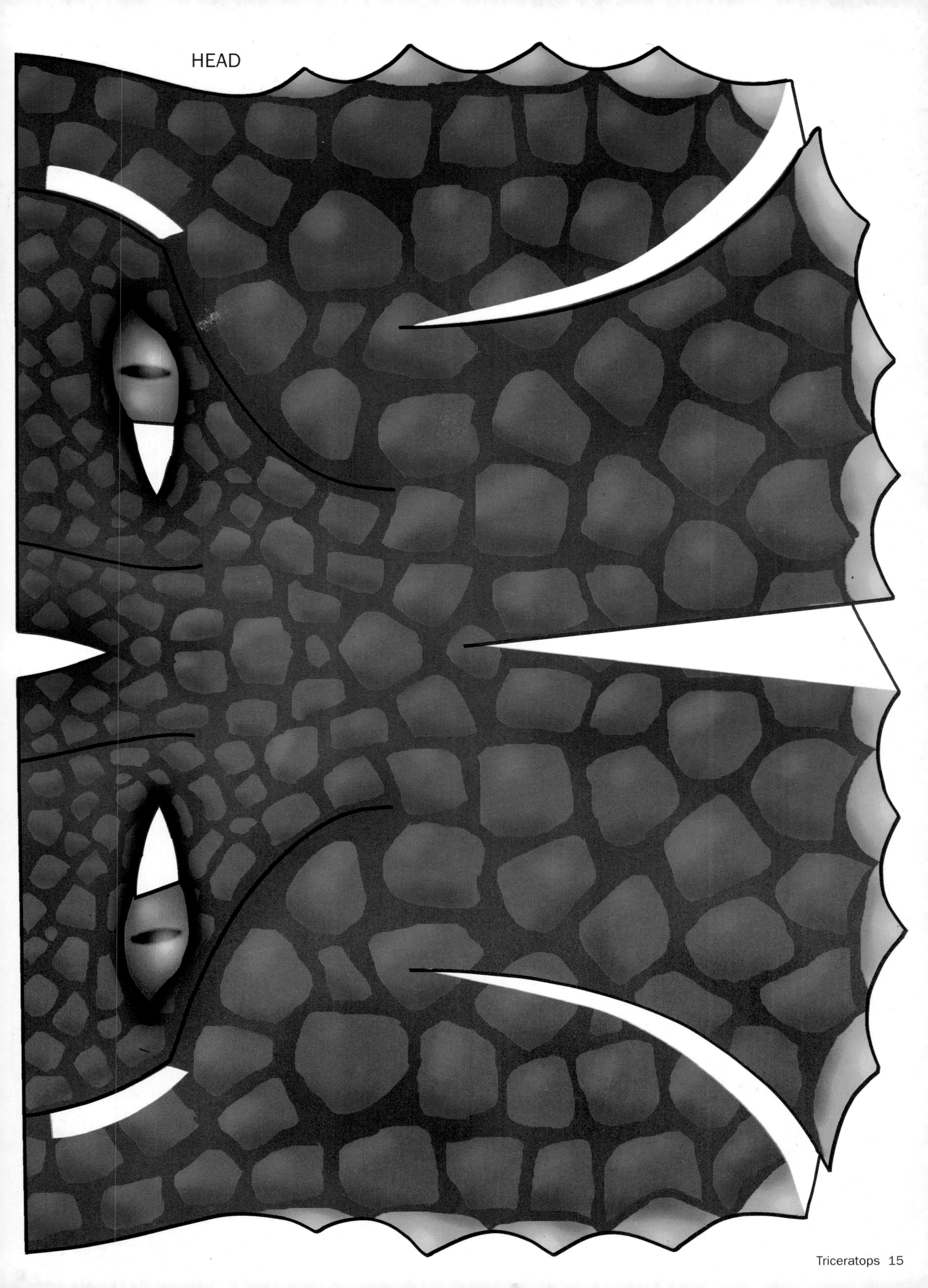
HEAD

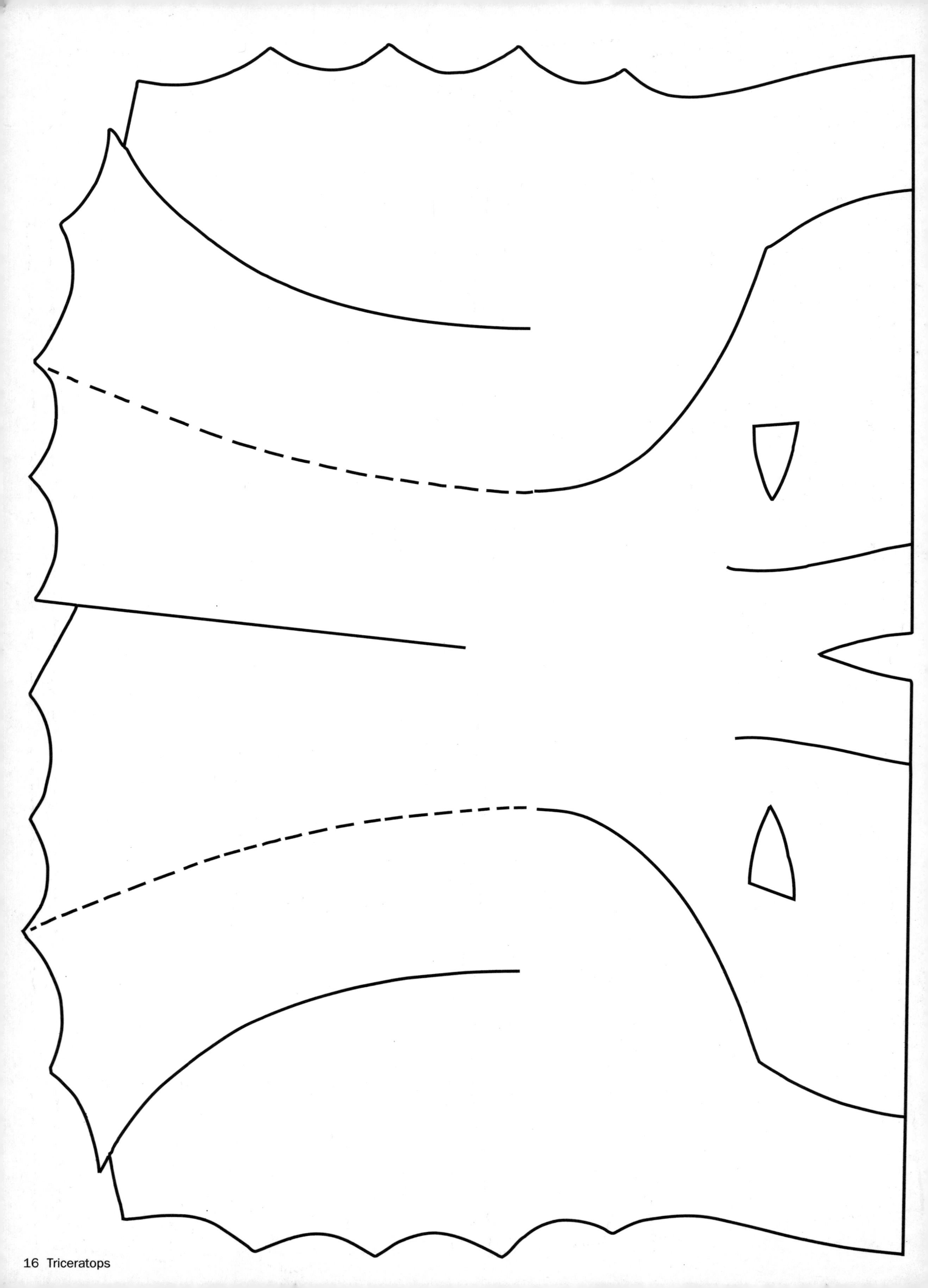

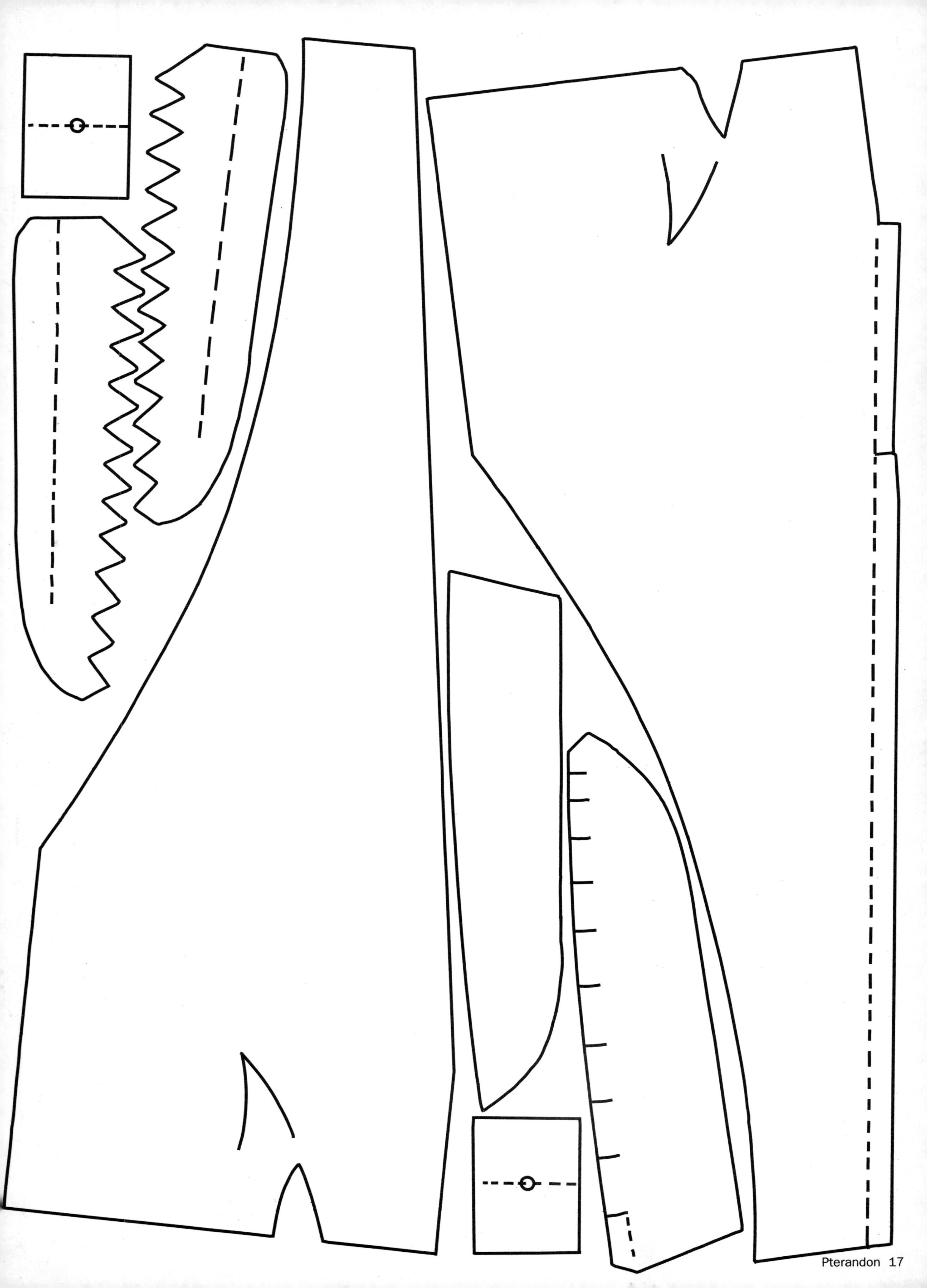

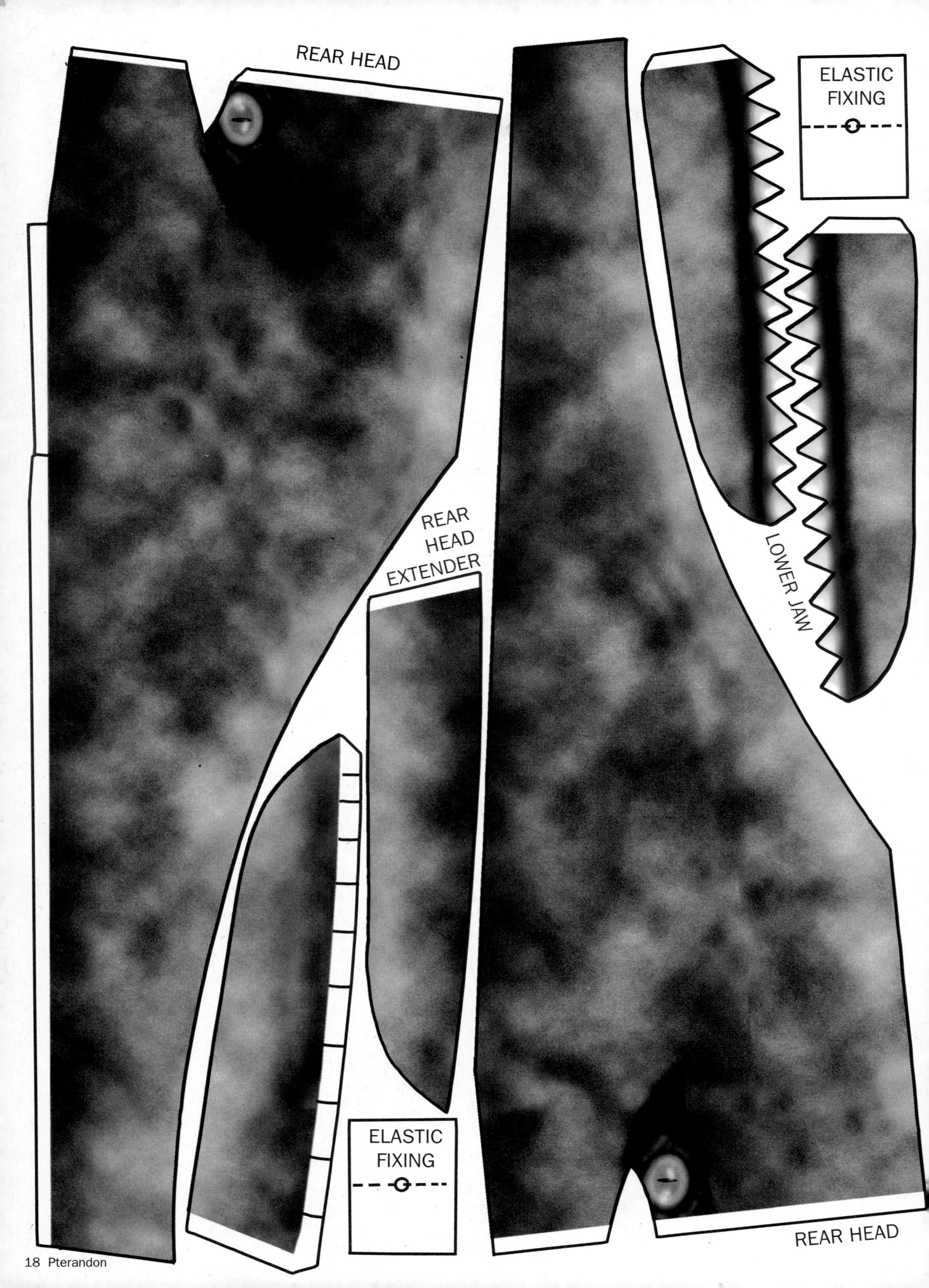
REAR HEAD
ELASTIC
FIXING
REAR
HEAD
EXTENDER
LOWER JAW
ELASTIC
FIXING
REAR HEAD

CENTRE HEAD

LOWER JAW

LOWER JAW

TOP JAW

TOP JAW

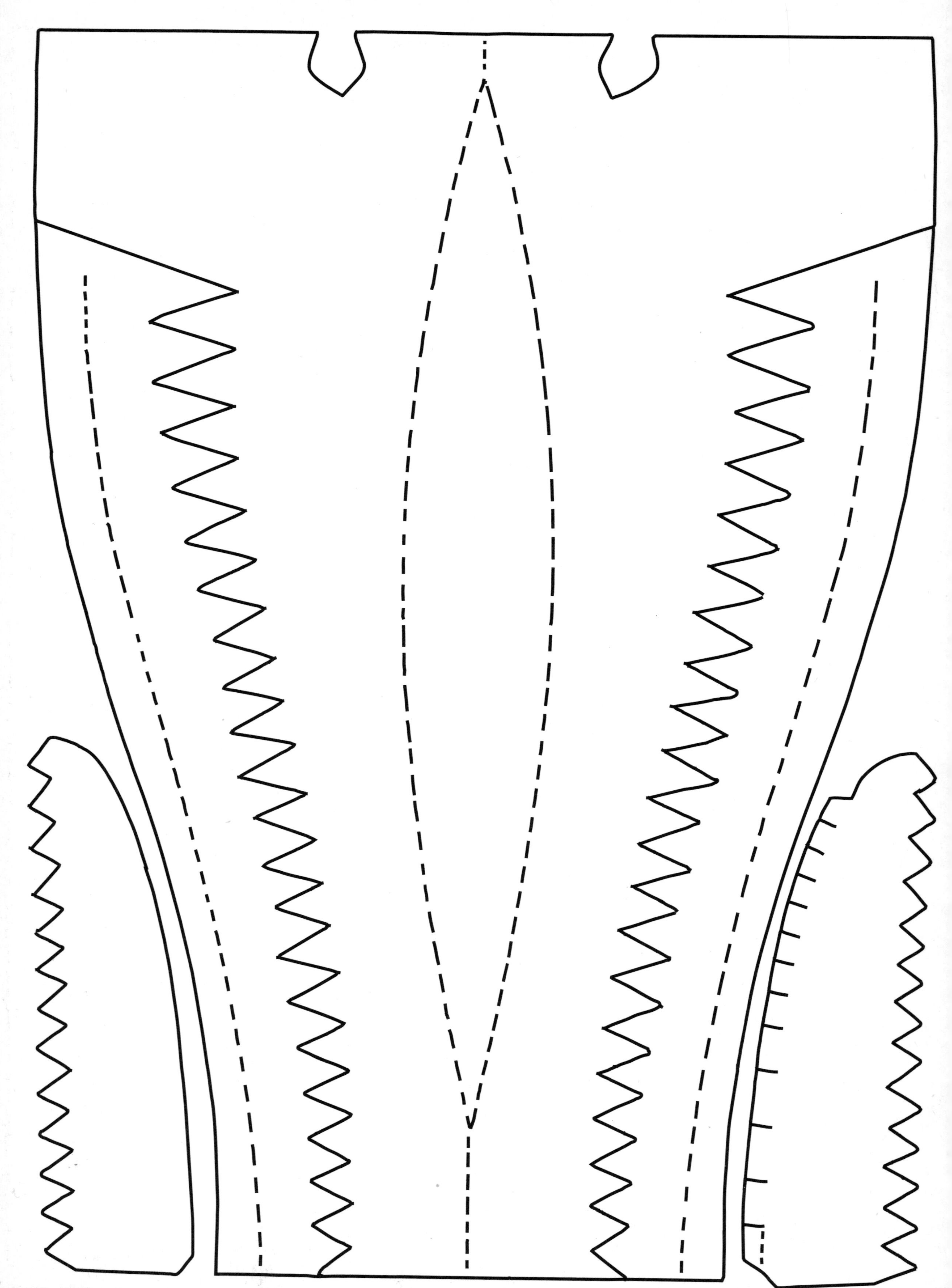

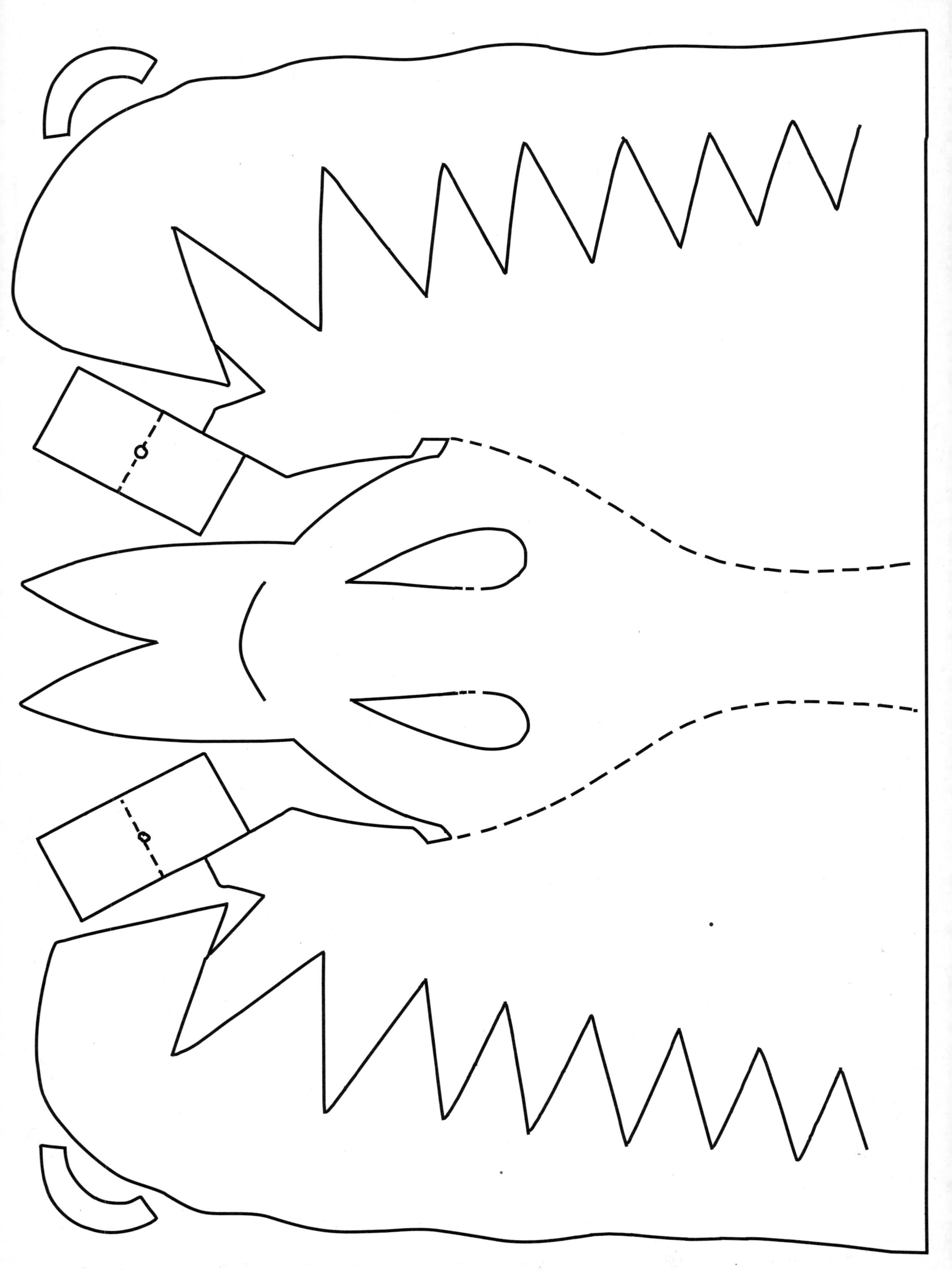

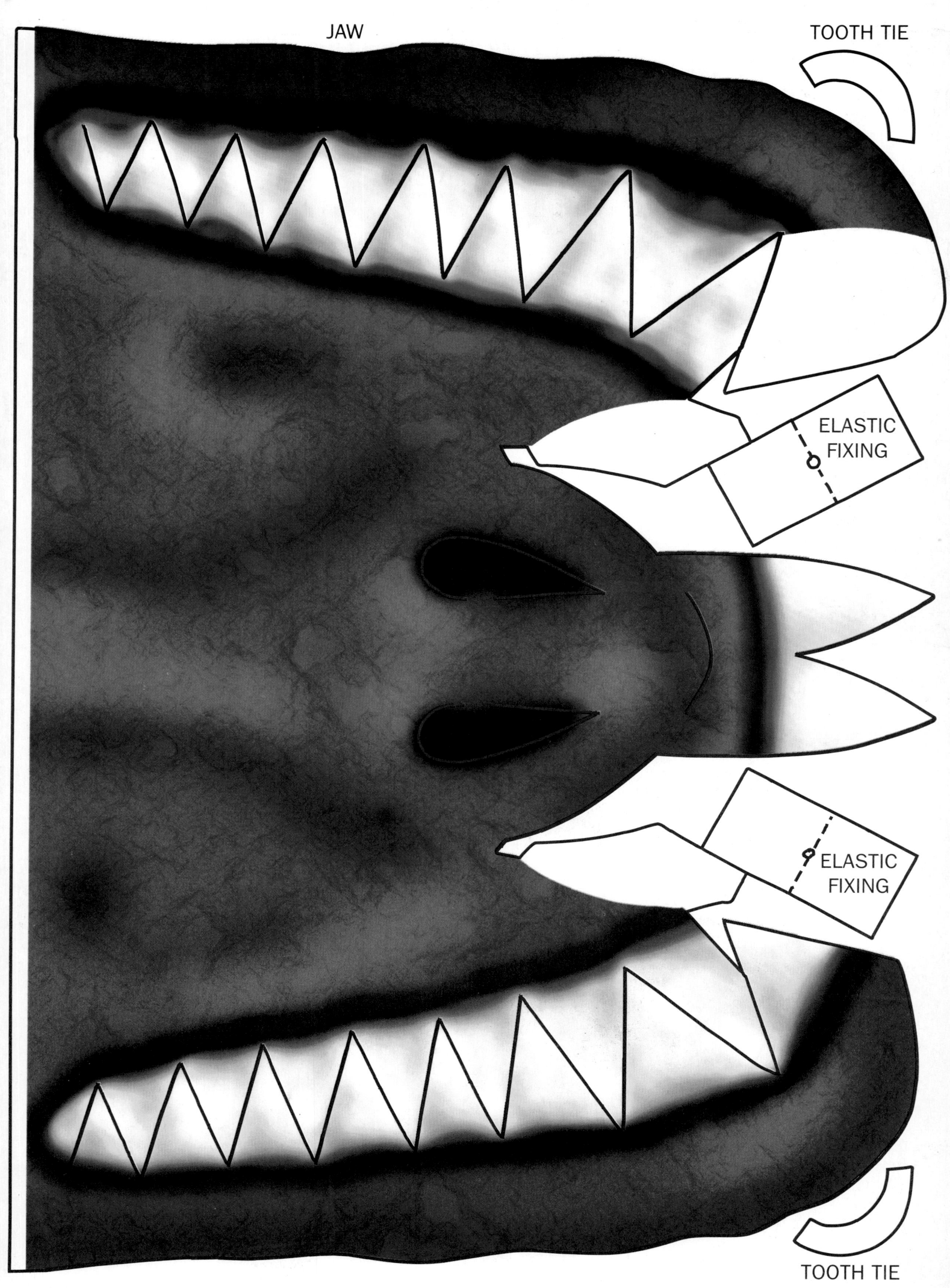
JAW
TOOTH TIE
ELASTIC FIXING
ELASTIC FIXING
TOOTH TIE

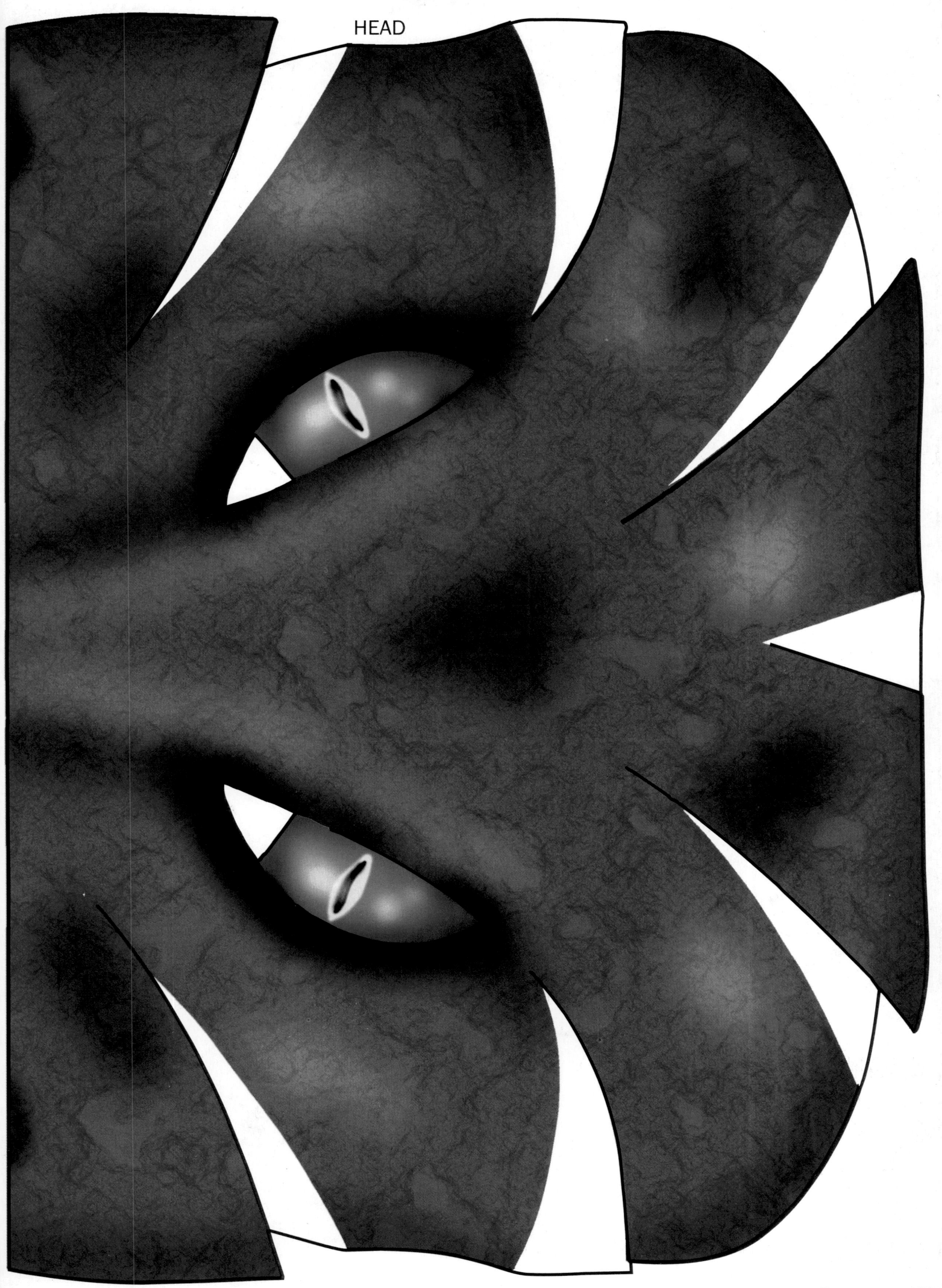
HEAD

Male Triceratops may also have fought other males with their horns, much as stags do battle today with their antlers. Palaeontologists have found the bones of many Triceratops at the same site so it is almost certain that they lived in herds.

A Triceratops length was about nine metres (30 ft) and it may have weighed as much as 9 tonnes (9 tons). It lived mainly in drier upland areas, unlike many dinosaurs which liked swamps. The Triceratops generally ate tough leaves, skewering them with its sharp beak-like mouth and then grinding them with blunt teeth in its cheeks. Some scientists estimate they could run at speeds of up to 48 kph (30 mph). They were among the last dinosaurs to emerge about 100 million years ago, and seem also to have been among the last to become extinct.

Pterosaur

(tero-sawr)

The Pterosaurs differed from true dinosaurs in that they did not live on the land but flew, or at least glided. Despite this, they lived at the same time as the other dinosaurs. The name Pterosaur applies to a group of flying reptiles, who lived between 150 and 70 million years ago.

Pterosaurs are the ancestors of today's birds, but, unlike birds, they never developed feathers. Instead, they formed wings on their upper or forward legs from stretched skin, as bats do. They probably glided, making use of thermals (upward currents of warm air), rather than flew. They had compact bodies but long skulls, sometimes as long as 1 metre (3 ft 4 ins). They were all lightly built and some had a wing span of 8 metres (25 ft), which makes them by far the largest creature ever to have flown above the earth.

Tyrannosaurus

(Ti-ran-oh-saw-rus)

One of the most formidable creatures to ever walk the earth, Tyrannosaurus ('tyrant lizard') was the greatest of the flesh-eating dinosaurs, called carnosaurs. It was about 12 metres (40 ft) long with a jaw measuring about 1 metre (39 ins). Each of its teeth was15 centimetres (6 ins) in length. Its mighty head and body were balanced by a long, powerful tail. A Tyrannosaurus would have been able to swallow a human being whole. An adult Tyrannosaurus weighed up to 7 tonnes (7 tons). It prowled wooded landscapes about 70 million years ago. When it had got its prey on the ground, Tyrannosaurus pinned it down with its huge feet and ate it.

Walking upright on its three-toed feet, a roaring Tyrannosaurus must have been an awesome sight. Scientists dispute whether Tyrannosaurus could move fast. Its weight suggests a lumbering creature, but its bones were incredibly strong. There are heavy animals alive today, like the rhinoceros, which can move very quickly. The Tyrannosaurus could therefore have been a great hunter.

Where are They Now?

All the dinosaurs died about 65 million years ago. The cause of their extinction remains one of the great unsolved mysteries of science.

Dinosaurs Today

For years people suspected that small dinosaurs still walked the earth, hidden in dense jungle or the rocky terrain of a mountainside. This led to dinosaur-hunting expeditions in the 19th century, but no live land dinosaurs were ever discovered. Nor are you likely to find any dinosaur bones on a country walk although it might be fun to try digging for other fossils.

If you want to see a dinosaur, it is better to visit a museum. Local museums often display the remains of dinosaurs discovered in the area. They may even display entire skeletons, or replicas.

Dinosaur skeletons in museums are held in place by a metal frame, for they all lack some bones. Any gaps can be filled in with plaster models. Reconstruction is skilled and time consuming work.

Did You Know?

- In a 6 kilometre (4 mile) stretch of Peace River Canyon, Canada, there are over 1,700 footprints made by 10 different dinosaurs.

- One Barosaurus skeleton discovered in North America had 64 gastroliths or stones between its ribs. When the fossil of a Coelophysis was unearthed it revealed that its last meal was one of its own babies. This is the only record of cannibalism among dinosaurs so far found.

- A footprint of a giant Apatosaurus holds 95 litres (20 gallons) of water, enough to fill a bath.

- Evidence from some fossil dinosaur eggs proved that babies grew up to 50 centimetres (1 ft 8 ins) in length before they hatched.

- It took 20 people more than three years to fit together the skeleton of a single Diplodocus.

- In the Gobi desert, a nest made by a Protoceratops with 20 eggs upright in layered circles proved that the mother must have rotated as she produced them.

- A mass grave unearthed in Montana, USA, contained the bones of over 10,000 Maiasaura dinosaurs. The herd was wiped-out by a volcanic eruption.

How to Make the Masks

ASK AN ADULT TO HELP YOU AND TAKE CARE WHEN USING SHARP KNIVES AND SCISSORS.

You will need:

▷ Small pair of sharp scissors or a craft knife with renewable blades;

▷ a ballpoint pen that has run out of ink (to make the creases);

▷ a small tube of contact adhesive glue (the sort that is put onto each surface to be stuck);

▷ carpenter's water-soluble glue (often referred to as PVA glue);

▷ some lengths of black or white cord elastic to secure the masks around the head.

Remove the model pages from the book. Read the instructions and look at the drawings to ensure you understand the assembly stages before starting to cut the parts. If you are not sure, go back over the instructions.

Work in a well-lit area where you can leave your model parts without them being damaged. Use a plastic cutting board or a thick sheet of cardboard to protect furniture.

You will find the cutting lines around the colour areas in a solid black line. Where the colour is very dark, the cutting lines are in white so that they are clearly visible. Try to cut to the edge of the black or white lines so that you will not see fragments of them on the finished mask.

The cutting lines are on the coloured side of the cardboard. On the reverse of each sheet, we have marked grey outlines (but do not use these for cutting lines) and dotted lines. These dotted lines show you where to fold the card. They have been positioned on the reverse so that they will not be visible on the finished masks. Put in the creases from the reverse.

Cut all solid lines. Crease all dotted lines.

Before you cut, double check that you are doing it correctly. Once you have cut, there is no going back. Only cut out and crease the parts as you need them in assembly - do not cut out all the pieces at once as you may then find it more difficult to follow the instructions.

Cutting Instructions

Use scissors where possible. If you need to use a craft knife, please ask an adult to do it for you – or to supervise you while you do it.

If using a craft knife, do not use blunt blades. Never place your hands or fingers in the line of your cut – always keep them to the side in case the blade slips. Try not to cut alongside plastic rulers or set squares – use steel edges instead (blades can catch the edge of plastic and run across onto the hand). Cut slowly along the solid black lines and press just firmly enough to cut through the card.

Don't forget to cut the small slits on the glue flaps where marked – these will enable you to curve pieces to shape.

Creasing Instructions

Crease each part as required after it has been cut out. Use the ballpoint pen to make the creases by running its nib along the dotted line gently to make a mark, and then going over it again to make a deeper crease. Try this on a piece of scrap paper first to see how it works.

Gluing Instructions

Do not apply glue straight from the tube. Use a strip of thick card like a narrow brush to spread the glue exactly where it is needed on the white glue areas. Use these areas line up the parts before pressing them into place. Take your time, don't rush, and check every step first.

Left and Right refers to the mask as worn on the face.

NB. Left and Right refers to the Mask as worn on the face.

Dilophosaurus Mask

(Crested Dinosaur, see page 9-12)

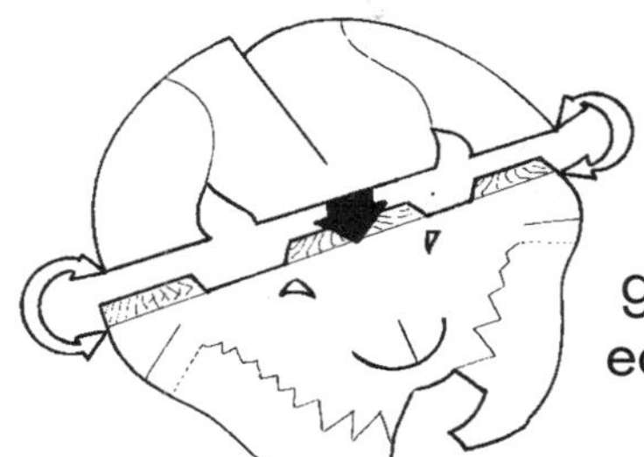

1. Glue Rear Head onto Front Head, carefully lining up glue area and side edges as shown.

2. Overlap and glue centre cut in Rear Head as arrowed at A. Crease along dotted lines in Rear and Front Head. Glue flaps arrowed at B each side, pressing inwards to make two concave 'cheek' areas. Overlap and glue flaps as arrowed at C. Shape jaw by gluing flaps as arrowed at D and E. Crease along dotted lines at back of jaw each side. Curve teeth outwards slightly.

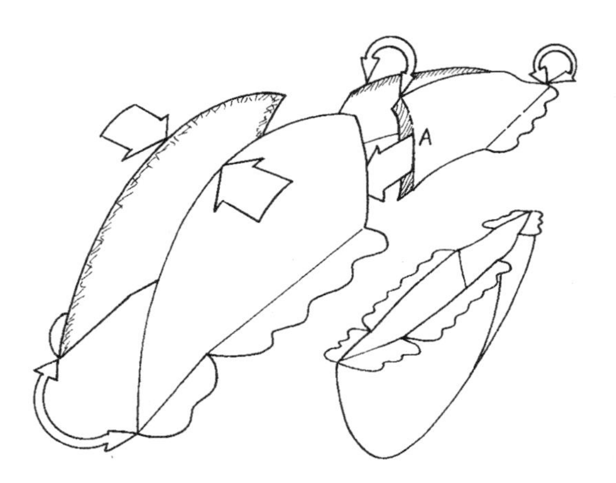

3. Gently curve Right and Left parts of Front Crest to make finished Crest slightly convex. Check that they match and glue together along curved edge. Apply glue sparingly to one edge only. Fold out wavy edged glue-flaps. Repeat process with Rear Crest. Glue Front and Rear Crests together as arrowed at A.

4. Glue completed Crest to top of Head as shown. Glue positions show how Crest is splayed at the centre, narrowing at rear. Line up carefully as arrowed at A. Glue Left and Right Eyes in position as arrowed at B. To help hold the teeth in position, glue Tooth Ties to inside of mask each side, positioning on Teeth as arrowed.

5. Cut two lengths of cord elastic, sufficient to fix at each side of mask and tie at back of head. Fold Elastic Fixings to shape. Thread elastic through hole as shown and tie knot. Pull elastic so that knot is inside flaps, and glue flaps together. Glue Fixings in position as shown. Tie elastic to comfortable fit with mask in position.

Triceratops Mask

(see pages 13-16)

On this mask only, some pieces are labelled on the reverse of the card.

1. Begin with the Head, overlapping and gluing the central cut at A.
Crease along dotted lines on either side of the central cut.
Overlap and glue flaps at B and C, pushing in slightly to form concave areas around the temples as arrowed. This overlapping and gluing pulls the mask into shape.
Glue Left and Right Side Plates under edge of Head as arrowed at D and E.
Overlap and glue flaps on Left and Right Middle Head parts as arrowed. This causes them to curve.
Glue Left and Right Middle Head parts under edge of Head as arrowed at F and G.

2. Glue both sides of Jaw in position, over glue flaps of Left and Right Middle Head parts and under Head as arrowed. (NB.For clarity, right hand parts have not been shown.)
Curve Side Plates in, and glue under Middle Head sections as arrowed. Curve up lower flaps of Jaw and glue as arrowed at A both sides.
Overlap and glue long cut in base of Jaw.

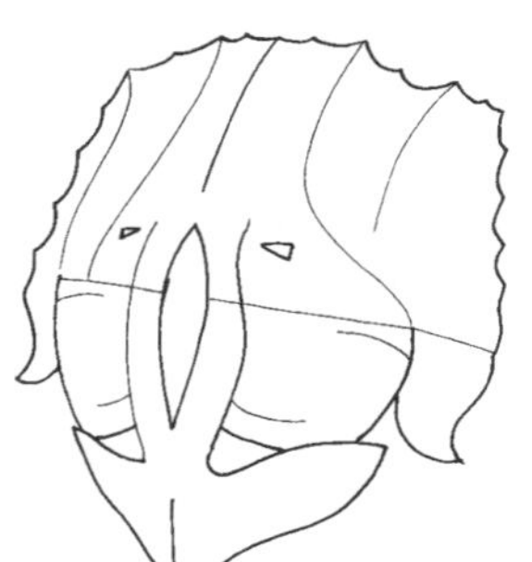

3. Mask now looks like this.

4. Crease both parts of the Nose Horn along dotted lines. Glue their edges together as shown, applying glue sparingly along edges of one part only. Wipe off excess when almost dry.
The completed horn is shown at A. Fold out small glue flaps.

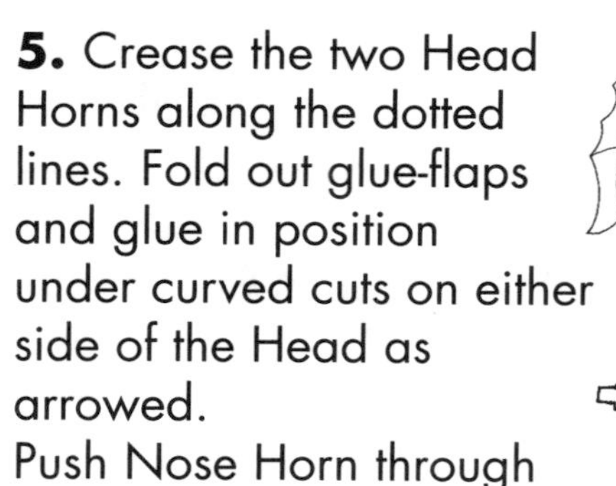

5. Crease the two Head Horns along the dotted lines. Fold out glue-flaps and glue in position under curved cuts on either side of the Head as arrowed.
Push Nose Horn through opening in Head and Jaw, and glue in position as shown. Glue both parts of Small Horn together and glue in position at base of Nose Horn as arrowed.

6. Completed mask looks like this.

7. Cut two lengths of cord elastic, sufficient to fix at each side of mask and tie at back of head. Fold Elastic Fixings to shape. Thread elastic through hole as shown. Pull elastic so that knot is inside flaps, and glue flaps together. Glue Fixings to inside of mask in positions as shown.
Tie elastic to comfortable fit with mask in position.

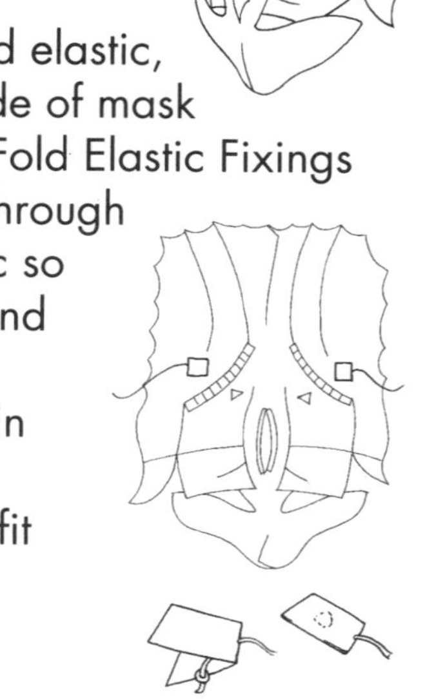

NB. Left and Right refers to the Mask as worn on the face.

Pterosaur Mask

(Flying Reptile, see pages 17-20)

1. Fold long glue flap on top of of Rear Head and glue to other half as arrowed. Glue the sides of the Rear Head Extender together along the glue-flaps, then glue it into the narrow end of the Rear Head as arrowed at A.

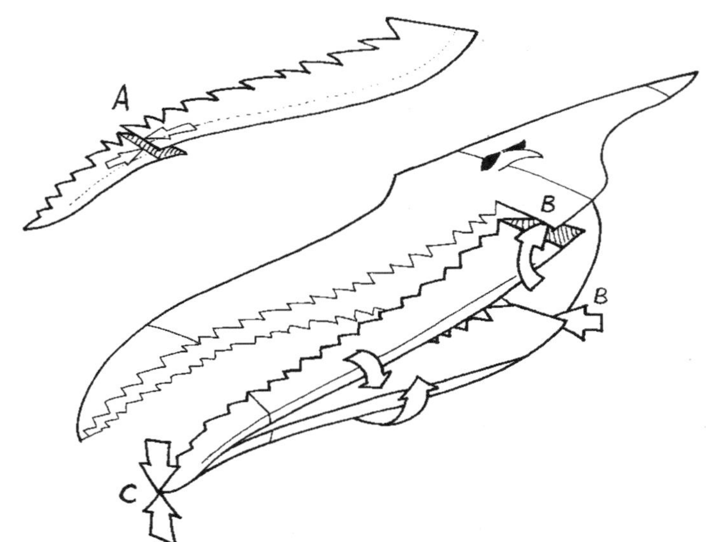

2. Cut out the Centre Head, noting that by cutting along the teeth you create the two long sections of the Lower Jaw. The Centre Head has two curved creases down the centre which create a flat area down the middle of the mask. Make these creases along the dotted lines and gently curve to shape as arrowed. Glue both halves of the Top Jaw together along the glue-flaps, glue the tips together then glue the completed part into the front of the Centre Head as arrowed at B.

4. Glue the long and short sections of the left side Lower Jaw together as arrowed at A. Repeat for right side. Lay the two completed halves of the Lower Jaw on top of each other, and glue the tips together as arrowed at C. Glue the Lower Jaw into the Centre Head each side as arrowed at B. Make the long crease along each half of the Lower Jaw as marked by the dotted line. (Arrows show the direction of the crease) This helps keep the section in shape.

3. Glue both completed sections of the Head together, lining up the edges carefully as arrowed.
Bend the corners of the eyes outward slightly.

5. Cut two lengths of cord elastic, sufficient to fix at each side of mask and tie at back of head.
Fold Elastic Fixings to shape.
Thread elastic through hole as shown and tie knot. Pull elastic so that knot is inside flaps, and glue flaps together. Glue Fixings in position as shown. Tie elastic to comfortable fit with mask in position.

NB. Left and Right refers to the Mask as worn on the face.

Tyrannosaurus Mask

(see pages 21-24)

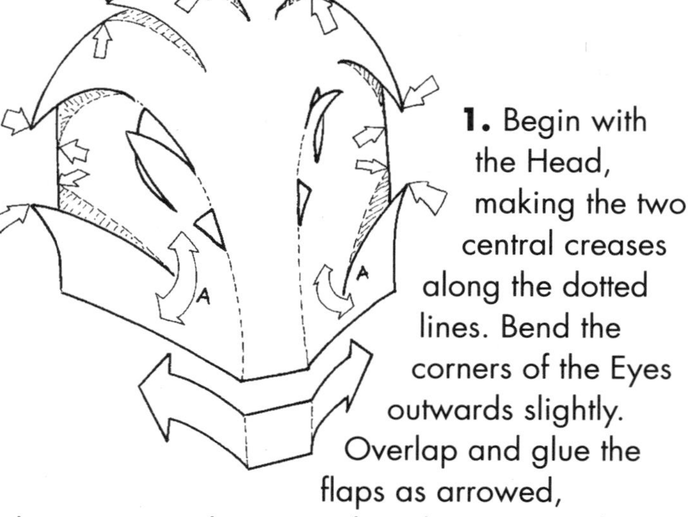

1. Begin with the Head, making the two central creases along the dotted lines. Bend the corners of the Eyes outwards slightly. Overlap and glue the flaps as arrowed, beginning at the top and working outwards. This overlapping and gluing pulls the mask into shape. Gluing the flaps arrowed at A creates a concave area below the eyes.

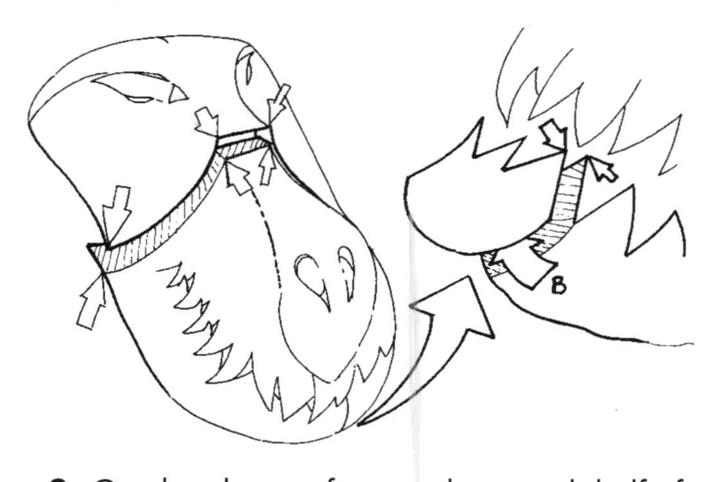

3. Overlap the two front teeth on each half of the Lower Jaw and glue as arrowed at B. Glue the Jaws and the Head together as shown. Ensure that the pieces line up exactly.

2. Make the two central creases in the Jaws. Fold in the flaps arrowed at A and glue in position beneath the nostrils, lining up the pieces at the teeth. Push in and curve the two nostril openings.

4. Two Tooth Ties help support the Jaws. Use these to join the teeth, gluing to the inside of the mask as arrowed at A. Curve the remaining teeth gently outwards.

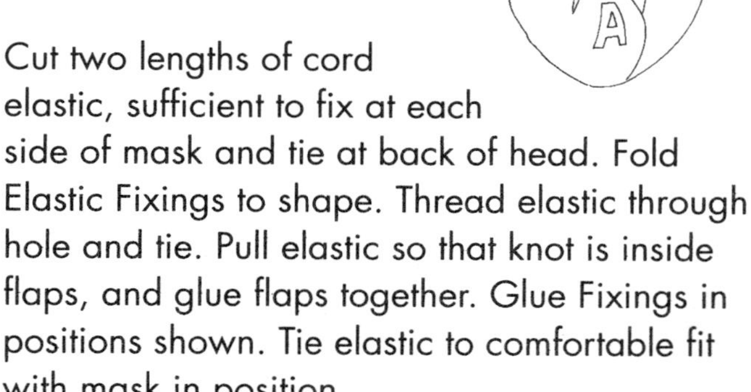

Cut two lengths of cord elastic, sufficient to fix at each side of mask and tie at back of head. Fold Elastic Fixings to shape. Thread elastic through hole and tie. Pull elastic so that knot is inside flaps, and glue flaps together. Glue Fixings in positions shown. Tie elastic to comfortable fit with mask in position.

First published in Great Britain in 1995 by Parragon Book Service Ltd, Units 13-17, Avonbridge Trading Estate, Atlantic Road, Avonmouth, Bristol BS11 9QD.

ISBN 0-7525-1086-X. Printed in Great Britain